The Stream Team Get It Clean!

Story and lyrics by Bill Northcote

Illustrations by Bill Northcote copyright © 2021

ISBN 978-1-3999-0188-8

Contact: streamteamclean@gmail.com

Not far from here there is a stream,
that slowly runs clear and clean.

In the stream lives a small school
of bubble blowing bream.

Bream are fish and when they
grow big they are shaped like a dish.

There is also an old frog called Grogg,
who loves to relax on his favourite log.

Frogs can jump quite far,
if they were as big as you they could
jump over a car.

And here is Toot the smooth newt,
who can hold his breath and play the flute.

Newts can live in water and on land,
they're not very big so can sit on your hand.

Up early and out for a stroll,
it's Vinny the busy brown water vole.

A Vole looks like a mouse,
they dig a hole in the bank which
becomes their house.

As the weather gets hotter,
into the cool water dives Potter the otter.

An otter is about the size of a cat and has webbed feet.

Well how about that!

And here is TanTan the trout,
she's not very quiet and likes to SHOUT!

Trout have spots on their sides,
with a flick of their tails through the
water they glide.

Then one day some friends stopped
for a snack,
it's a pity they didn't take their
rubbish back.

By the stream drove a man in a van, who finished his drink and then threw out the can.

Two friends who are laughing and talking, they dropped their wrappers and carried on walking.

More and more litter was dropped
onto the bank,
it blew into the water and some
of it sank.

The clean stream has become a bog,
so now there sits a sad old frog.

Enough is enough!

The stream needed a clean.

So they all worked together
and became The Stream Team.

Now all the rubbish is cleared,
the happy team danced and cheered.

It would be such a shame if the stream was littered again.

But what can we do?

Well that really is up to me and you!

The Rubbish Rap

Ain't no big thing to put **litter** in the **bin**.

Dropping rubbish isn't **funny,**
it costs lots of **money.**

We can recycle paper, card and plastic,
it really is **fantastic.**

Nature is **great**, don't leave it in a **state**.

So don't be a **quitter**, bin your **litter**.

Bin boom bam, bin that **can!**

Bin boom bash, bin that **trash!**

BOOM!